REMBRANDT

(1606 - 1669)

MAJOR GRAPHIC WORKS

IT IS HARD TO DESCRIBE THE GREATEST PAINTER OF THE NORTH AND THE GREATEST PRINTMAKER OF THEM ALL, BECAUSE REMBRANDT IS SO MANY PEOPLE. TRY TO PIGEONHOLE HIM ANYWHERE, AND HE ESCAPES. CALL HIM A DUTCHMAN, AND HE SHOWS A DEEPER UNDERSTANDING OF THE ESSENTIALS OF THE ITALIAN HIGH RENAISSANCE THAN ANY NORTHERNER. CALL HIM A MASTER OF SHADOWS, AND HE DRAWS A FIGURE WITH THREE OR FOUR LINES. CALL HIM SPIRITUAL, AND HE THROWS GROSSNESS AT YOU.

A. HYATT MAYOR, 1971

No. 20 *Self-Portrait Drawing at a Window* (3ʳᵈ State)
Etching, drypoint & burin, 1648

R. S. JOHNSON FINE ART

645 N. MICHIGAN AVE., CHICAGO, IL 60611
(312) 943-1661 www.rsjohnsonfineart.com
Est. 1955

REMBRANDT HARMENSZ VAN RIJN

MAJOR GRAPHIC WORKS

*

Texts by R. Stanley Johnson

2014

Publication No. 166

*

ISBN No. 978-0-9913111-2-5
Library of Congress Cat. Card No. 2014915461
All Rights Reserved
No part of the contents of this publication
may be reproduced without written
consent from either its authors or
R. S. Johnson Fine Art
Published in 2014

*

-Research and Texts- Photography and Design-
R. Stanley Johnson
Ursula M. Johnson
Suzanne Varkalis
Anna Clark
Eric Leech

R. S. Johnson Fine Art would like to thank the collectors who
allowed us to include in this catalogue the following works from their collections:

No. 3 *A Beggar Seated on a Bank* (1st State), etching, 1630
No. 9 *Christ Driving the Money Changers from the Temple* (2nd State), etching, 1635
No. 13 *Death of the Virgin* (2nd State), etching with drypoint, 1639
No. 22 *Jews in the Synagogue* (2nd State), etching, 1648
No. 27 *Christ at Emmaus* (1st State), etching, 1654

On Cover:
No. 25 *Christ Crucified between Two Thieves: The Three Crosses* (3rd State)
Etching and drypoint, 1653

No. 30 *Jan Lutma, Goldsmith* (2nd State), 1656

I. CONNOISSEURSHIP IN REMBRANDT PRINTS

This publication reconsiders certain connoisseurship questions involving individual graphic works of Rembrandt van Rijn (1606 - 1669), works that over the centuries already have inspired an enormous amount of interest and research. The select group of works being considered here, all from private collections, includes some of the finest and most rare examples of Rembrandt's most celebrated graphic achievements.

Early in his career, Rembrandt concluded that printmaking, in its aesthetic and expressive possibilities, was at least the equal of drawing and painting. He went on to produce around three hundred etchings between 1628 and 1665. These works present unending experimentation on the part of Rembrandt in order to obtain the best expressions of his artistic feelings. The artist's endeavors in printmaking began with etching, to which he added engraving and still later drypoint.

Rembrandt as printmaker was prolific and innovative, producing works of traditional subjects with traditional materials in an often nontraditional and experimental manner. It is these particular experimental qualities, which make continuing Rembrandt scholarship so fascinating. These works are characterized by the artist's constant attempts to test the limits of printmaking. This testing of limits (use of different papers, inks, plate tones, etc.) was not to be sought to the same degree by any major artist until the appearance of the graphic works of Pablo Picasso three centuries later.

In 1952, Picasso's dealer D. H. Kahnweiler published "Huit Entretiens avec Picasso" (Eight Discussions with Picasso) in one of which (February 6, 1934) Picasso stated: "Imagine that I would make a portrait of Rembrandt. It would be one of those stories where the varnish suddenly jumped away and the plate was ruined. What was I to do with a ruined plate? I decided to continue etching. The work gradually turned into a Rembrandt! It began to please me. I continued etching in order to search for those blacks of Rembrandt, which are not to be obtained in a single try."

For each Rembrandt etching, in addition to basic research, questions of condition also must be taken into consideration: freshness of impression, fullness of margins, presence of particular watermarks, moisture or sun damage and traces of restoration. The more rare and more beautiful a given impression, the more logically a connoisseur would be willing to accept a degree of condition problems. In judgmental decisions, the experience and sensitivity of a connoisseur's eye and personal taste in the end also become critical. Knowledge of all of these considerations adds to our enjoyment in contemplating and appreciating the works of this great Master.

(text continues on page 6)

II. REMBRANDT RESEARCH

Research on Rembrandt is a long established discipline in the history of art. Scholarly consideration of Rembrandt's printmaking began in Paris in 1751 with Edmé-François Gersaint's Rembrandt print catalogue raisonné. This was followed forty-six years later in 1797 in Vienna with Adam Bartsch's two volumes: *Le Peintre Graveur: Catalogue Raisonné de toutes les estampes qui Forment l'Oeuvre de Rembrandt.* Other early attempts at a complete analysis of Rembrandt prints include the studies by Charles Henry Middleton (London, 1878), Francis Seymour Haden (London, 1879), Eugene Duthuit (Paris, 1883), Woldemar von Seidlitz (Leipzig 1895), Arthur Hind (London, 1923) and Ludwig Münz (London, 1952).

In further exploration of individual impressions of Rembrandt prints, the study by Osbert Barnard and George Biörklund, published in 1968, attempts to establish a chronological order to identify the year each work was produced and also the order in which each print was created in a given year. Thus their reference "35-C" for Rembrandt's etching *The Great Jewish Bride* (our catalogue No. 7), the "35" refers to the year of execution (1635) and the "C" indicates that it was the third etching created by Rembrandt in that year. Referring to watermarks, the 1998 study, *Watermarks in Rembrandt's Prints*, by Nancy Ash and Shelley Fletcher (including Jan Piet Filedt Kok's enlightening essay "Watermark Research: Its Significance in Studying Rembrandt's Etchings") is crucial in identifying the manufacture dates of papers used by Rembrandt, which in turn leads to more accurate dating of individual impressions. Understanding the varied natures of different inks and papers, with different watermarks, is essential in evaluating and dating impressions of various states from each Rembrandt plate. Provenance is often revealing and the information provided in Frits Lugt's *Marques de Collection* published in Amsterdam in 1926 and then his *Supplément* published in La Hague in 1956 gives important information concerning different collector's marks.

Among more recent texts, White-Boon's *Rembrandt's Etchings* (2 Volumes), Amsterdam, 1969, has proved to be useful for the basic describing and cataloguing of particular etchings. The same could be said for *The Dutuit Collection* catalogue from the Petit Palais in Paris in 1986 and also for Filedt Kok's 1992 catalogue of the Amsterdam Rembrandt House holdings as well as the revised *Rembrandt House* catalogue by Eva Ornstein-Van Slooten and Marijke Holtrop in 2003. The joint publication of the British Museum and the Rijksmuseum in 2000, *Rembrandt The Printmaker* by Erik Hinterding, Ger Luijten and Martin Royalton-Kisch, also is insightful, as is the New York Metropolitan Museum of Art's publication from 1995, *Rembrandt/ Not Rembrandt*, with texts by Von Sonnenburg, Liedtke, Logan, Dickey and specifically Orenstein's essay: "Rembrandt Prints and the Questions of Attribution". Additionally, Clifford Ackley's two instructive texts: *Printmaking in the Age of Rembrandt* (1981) and *Rembrandt's Journey: Painter, Draftsman, Etcher* (2004) are instrumental in continued study. The excellent texts and extensive new research by Gisèle Lambert and Eléna Santiago Páez in *Rembrandt: La lumière de l'ombre*, Bibliothèque Nationale, Paris and Fundacio Caixa Catalunya, Barcelona 2005, add still more information. Finally, in 2013, Erik Hinterding and Jaco Rutgers published *The New Hollstein: Dutch & Flemish Etchings, Engravings and Woodcuts.* This publication attempts to provide all the most recent research regarding states, dates, watermarks and collector's marks and includes illustrations of the different known states for each Rembrandt etching. This latter publication is now our own primary basis for describing and cataloguing graphic works by Rembrandt.

R. Stanley Johnson
September, 2014

SELECTED REFERENCES

Ackley, Clifford S. *Printmaking in the Age of Rembrandt*, Museum of Fine Arts, Boston, 1981. Clifford Ackley. *Rembrandt's Journey: Painter, Draftsman, Etcher*, Museum of Fine Art, Boston, Art Institute of Chicago, (texts also by Ronni Baer, Thomas E. Rassieur and William W. Robinson), 2004.

Alpers, Svetlana. *Rembrandt's Enterprise: The Studio and the Market*, The University of Chicago Press, 1988.

Ash, Nancy and Shelley Fletcher. *Watermarks in Rembrandt's Prints.* National Gallery of Art, Washington, D.C. 1998.

Bartsch, Adam. *Le Peintre Graveur Catalogue raisonné de toutes les estampes qui Forment l'Oeuvre de Rembrandt* (2 Volumes), Vienna, 1797.

Bartsch, Adam. *Le Peintre-graveur* (21 Volumes), Vienna, 1803-1821.

Begemann, Haverkamp. *Rembrandt after Three Hundred Years*, Art Institute of Chicago, 1969.

Benesch, Otto. *The Drawings of Rembrandt*, (6 Volumes), London. 1954-1957.

Biörklund, George with the assistance of Osbert H. Barnard. *Rembrandt's Etchings: True and False: A summary Catalogue in a Distinctive Chronological Order*, Stockholm and New York, 1968.

Boon, Karl. *Rembrandt Etchings*, Rijksmuseum, Amsterdam, Museum Boymans - Van Benningen, Rotterdam, 1956.

Burollet, Thérèse and Sophia Renouard de Bussierre. *Rembrandt Eaux-Fortes, La Collection Dutuit*, Musée du Petit Palais, Paris 1986.

Chapman, H. Perry. *Rembrandt's Self-Portraits*, Princeton University Press, 1990.

Dutuit, Eugène. *L'Oeuvre complet de Rembrandt*, Paris 1883.

Filedt Kok, Jan Piet. *Rembrandt Etchings and Drawings in the Rembrandt House,* 1992.

Filedt Kok, Jan Piet. "Watermark Research: Its Significance in Studying Rembrandt's Etchings," (in Ash and Fletcher, 1998) (see above).

Gersaint, Edmé-Francois. *Catalogue raisonné de toutes les pièces qui forment l'oeuvre de Rembrandt,* Paris, 1751.

Haden, Francis Seymour. *The Etched Work of Rembrandt: A Monograph*, London, 1879.

Hind, Arthur. *A Catalogue of Rembrandt Etchings*, London, 1923.

Hinterding, Erik. "The History of Rembrandt's Copper plates with a Catalogue of those that Survived", *Simulus* 22, 1993-1994.

Hinterding, Erik, Ger Luijten and Martin Royalton-Kisch. *Rembrandt the Printmaker*, British Museum, London in association with the Rijksmuseum, Amsterdam, 2000.

Hinterding, Erik and Jaco Rutgers. *Rembrandt: The New Hollstein Dutch & Flemish Etchings, Engravings and Woodcuts* (7 Volumes), Rijksmuseum Amsterdam, 2013.

Hollstein, E. W. H. *Dutch and Flemish Etchings* (58 Volumes), Amsterdam, 1949 2001.

Jean-Richard, Pierrette. *Rembrandt: Graveur et Dessins*, Le Louvre, Paris, 2000.

Johnson, R. Stanley. "Quelques Réflexions", *Nouvelles de l'Estampe,* Bibliothèque Nationale, Paris, March 1994.

Johnson, R. Stanley, *Old Master Prints: 1475-1825*, Chicago, 2004.

Lambert, Gisèle and Eléna Santiago Páez. *Rembrandt: La Lumière de l'ombre,* Bibliothèque National, Paris, and the Fundacio Caixa Catalunya, Barcelona, 2005.

Lugt, Frits. *Marques de Collections*, Amsterdam, 1921, and *Marques de Collections Supplément,* La Hague, 1956.

Luijten, Ger. "Falling Silent - Hanging Rembrandt's Prints", *Art on Paper*, May-June, 2001.

Mayor, A. Hyatt. *Prints and People: A Social History of Printed Pictures*, The Metropolitan Museum of Art, New York, 1971.

Middleton, Charles Henry. *A Descriptive Catalogue of the Etched Work of Rembrandt van Rijn*, London, 1878.

Münz, Ludwig. *Rembrandt's Etchings: Reproductions of the whole Original Etched Works* (2 Volumes), London, 1952.

Orenstein, Nadine M. "Rembrandt's Prints and the Question of Attribution," pp. 201-245 in *Rembrandt/Not Rembrandt*, Metropolitan Museum of Art, New York, 1995.

Schama, Simon M. "A Different Jerusalem: The Jews in Rembrandt's Amsterdam," in *The Jews in the Age of Rembrandt's Amsterdam*, Judaic Museum, Washington D.C., 1981-1982.

Seidlitz, Woldemar von. *Kritisches Verzeichnis der Radierung Rembrandts,* Leipzig, 1895.

Slive, Seymour. *Rembrandt and His Critics 1630-1730*, The Hague, 1953.

Slooten, Eva Ornstein-Van and Marijke Holtrop. *The Rembrandt House: Revised.* Amsterdam, 2004.

Sonnenburg, Hubert von with Walter Liedtke, Carolyn Logan, Nadine M. Orenstein and Stephanie S. Dickey, *Rembrandt/Not Rembrandt in the Metropolitan Museum of Art: Aspects of Connoisseurship*, (2 Volumes), The Metropolitan Museum of Art, New York, 1995.

White, Christopher and Karel G. Boon. *Rembrandt's Etchings* (2 Volumes), Amsterdam, 1969.

CATALOGUE

1. ***The Artist's Mother, Head and Bust: Three Quarters Right*** (2nd State), 1628

Etching
65 x 63 mm.; 2 1/2 x 2 2/5 inches

Provenance:
Graf von Lepell (1755-1826)(Lugt 1672)
Charles Delenglade (born 1870)(Lugt 660)
Kupferstich Kabinet der Staatlichen Museen (Berlin) (Lugt 1606 & 2398)

References:
Bartsch 354-II/II
Hind 1-I/II or II/II
Barnard-Biörklund 28-H
New Hollstein 5-II/IV

Notes:
1. Clifford Ackley has described this etching, apparently Rembrandt's first graphic work and presumably depicting the mother of the artist (Clifford S. Ackley, *Rembrandt's Journey*, Museum of Fine Arts, Boston, 2004, page 86):

    > [Rembrandt] mapped every irregularity of the old woman's skin, combining the minute description of the old woman's facial features with a shorthand indication of her clothing. The vivid realism of her face thus is enhanced by the contrast with the scribbled sketchiness of her clothing. Conventional portrait engravers applied their talent toward the replication of furs, knots and folds, but Rembrandt merely hints at the clothing and directs our attention to the woman's face.

2. Early impressions, such as this one appear to have light drypoint scratches above the left eye and on the sleeve to the left. Since this impression is signed and dated in the plate, it is here catalogued as a second state. The New Hollstein notes that in the following third state, vertical lines are added to the backs of his mother's head at the level of her eyes.

3. The collector Graf von Lepell (1755 - 1826) was an art historian who published a catalogue raisonné on Claude Lorrain, a catalogue on the works of Albrecht Dürer and in 1825 one on Raphael entitled *Übersicht der Gemälde Raphaels*. Upon his death, Lepell left his collection to the King of Prussia, Friedrich Wilhelm III.

2. *A Beggar Seated on a Bank* (1st State), 1630

Etching
117 x 70 mm.; 4 5/8 x 2 3/4 inches

Provenance:
K-F. F. von Nagler (1770 - 1846) (Lugt 2529)
Neville D. Goldschmid (1814 - 1875) (Lugt 1962)
Kupferstichkabinett der Staatlichen Museen, Berlin (Lugt 1606) and with their duplicate stamp (Lugt 2398)
Rud. Ph. Goldschmidt (1840 - 1914) (Lugt 2926)
Dr. Otto Schäfer (not in Lugt)
R. S. Johnson Fine Art, 2007

References:
Bartsch 174
Hind 111
Barnard-Biörklund 30-B
New Hollstein 50 I/II

Notes:
1. A fine, early impression with the vertical polishing scratches still quite visible. Trimmed just inside the platemark.
2. The young beggar, as noted by Hind, bears a strong resemblance to Rembrandt himself, particularly his etching, also from 1630, *Self-Portrait, Open-Mouthed* (Bartsch 13). In both works, the subject's mouths are open, showing a few teeth, both foreheads creased in frowns. Peter Shathorn noted in *Rembrandt: The Printmaker* (British Museum Press, 2000, page 94), that in this as well as other related etchings, Rembrandt has found his model from the series of beggar prints by Jacques Callot (1592 - 1635). Specifically in this work, the beggar's open mouth and begging hand are found in one of Callot's standing figures (Lieure, Volume VII, figures 479-503). Shathorn also notes that the artist found inspiration for his rocky bank in an engraving by Lucas van Leyden (1494 - 1553), see: *The New Hollstein, Lucas van Leyden*, No. 143.
3. The New Hollstein notes that in early impressions, there are rough, uneven plate edges. In later impressions, two horizontal scratches appear over the man's right foot.
4. The provenance of this work includes some of the great collectors of Old Master prints over the last two hundred years:

   A. Karl Ferdinand Friedrich von Nagler (born in Bavaria in 1770) was, according to Lugt, a great collector of Dürer and Rembrandt, as well as portraits by Le Blon. He was closely associated with the King of Prussia, by whom he was named first Postmaster general.
   B. Neville D. Goldschmid (1814 - 1875) was the British Director of Goldschmid & Co., a Paris based gas supply company, with activities center in La Hague in Holland. He became the owner of a tramway company following the opening of an art gallery, in which he sold off his collection of "Modern"

(text continues on page 14)

(19th century) paintings in order to concentrate on Old Masters. His collection of Old Master paintings included Vermeer's *Diana*, now one of the masterworks at the museum in La Hague. Goldschmid collected Old Master Prints and probably bought this Rembrandt directly from von Nagler.

C. Rudolf Philip Goldschmidt (1840 - 1914) was the son of a Frankfurt banker, who early in his career, moved to Berlin. His collection, which merits an entire page in Lugt's book on collector's marks, concentrated on 17th century Dutch prints and drawings, with special interest in Rembrandt.

D. Dr. Otto Schäfer is considered one of Germany's most astute 20th-century collectors of Old Master prints. His collection concentrated predominately on Schongauer, Dürer and Rembrandt.

Collection:
Private Collection, Philadelphia

3. **Self-Portrait, Frowning: Bust** (3rd State), 1630

Etching
70 x 60 mm.; 2 3/4 x 2 3/8 inches

References:
Bartsch 10-III/III
Hind 30
Barnard-Biörklund 30-M
New Hollstein 68 III/III

Notes:
1. In this fine, early self-portrait when the artist was only twenty-four years old, Rembrandt looks himself in the eye with an angry stare.
2. This is one of several small and now rare self-portrait etchings, which Rembrandt executed around 1630, others are: *Self-Portrait with Beret* (1630) and *Wide-Eyed; Self-Portrait Laughing* (1633).
3. This is a third state since the horizontal lines crossing the upper plate are burnished out.

4. *Self-Portrait with Plumed cap and Lowered Sabre* (2nd State), 1634

Etching
130 x 108 mm.; 5 1/16 x 4 1/4 inches

Provenance:
Collection of Walter Johnston

References:
Bartsch 23-II/III
Hind 110
Barnard-Biörklund 34-B
New Hollstein 135-II/III

Notes:
1. A very fine impression of the second state. In the first state of this etching, Rembrandt presents himself in three-quarter length with plumed cap and lowered sword, 19.7 x 10.8 cm. in size. There appear to be only four known impressions of this first state; one at the Rijksmuseum in Amsterdam; one in the British Museum in London; one in the Bibliothèque Nationale in Paris and another in Paris in the Rothschild Collection.
2. In this very rare second state, the subject is reduced to an irregular oval, 13 x 10.8 cm. in size. It depicts only a bust-length portrait of the artist with added work in burin, shading the figure and the background. White-Boon (Christopher White & Karel Boon, *Rembrandt's Etchings: An Illustrated Catalogue*, Van Gendt & Co., Amsterdam, 1969, page 11) knew of only nine impressions of this second state, namely those at the Rijksmuseum in Amsterdam, Kupferstichkabinett in Berlin, Teylers Stichting in Haarlem, the Hermitage Museum in St. Petersburg, The British Museum in London, the Bibliothèque Nationale in Paris, the Duthuit Collection in Paris, the Rothschild Collection in Paris and the Albertina in Vienna.
3. In the following third state of this etching, Rembrandt made the irregular border into an exact oval. The third state of this work is also very rare and White-Boon know of only nine of these, including those at the Rijksmuseum in Amsterdam, the Kupferstichkabinett in Berlin, the Fitzwilliam Museum in Cambridge, Teylers Stichting in Haarlem, the Hermitage Museum in St. Petersburg, The British Museum in London, the Bibliothèque Nationale in Paris, the Duthuit Collection in Paris and the Albertina in Vienna.

5. **The Angel Appearing to the Shepherds** (3rd State), 1634

Etching, drypoint & burin
262 x 218 mm.; 10 5/16 x 8 9/16 inches

Watermark:
Arms of Württemberg B'.a. (Ash & Fletcher No. 9)

References:
Bartsch 44-III/III
Hind 120
Barnard-Biörklund 34-J
New Hollstein 125-III/III

Notes:
1. A very fine impression of the third state. This appears to be Rembrandt's earliest combination of etching, engraving (burin) and drypoint. In the first state, as seen in the impression at the British Museum, the central area is complete, while the rest of the composition is only lightly worked. This plate, very incomplete in the first state, was largely finished in the second state. In this third state, Rembrandt added shade to the upper branches of the dying tree, to the central figure directly below the tree, to the two distant cows on the right as well as to the wings and drapery of the angel.

2. *The Arms of Württemberg* watermark dates this impression to the early 1630s (Ash & Fletcher page 66). The identical watermark is found on an impression of: *Self-Portrait with Raised Sabre*, 1634, (Bartsch 18), Rijksmuseum Print Collection impression as well as in *The Good Samaritan*, 1633, (Bartsch 90), Museum of Fine Arts, Boston.

3. In this work, Rembrandt depicts the angel standing above, on a bank of clouds. Cherubs are emerging from the surrounding, celestial mists, while in the center of the blinding flash above, the Dove of the Holy Spirit appear; the frightened shepherds are seen below.

4. When Rembrandt's prints are highly finished, as in this case, they are usually influenced by a painted precedent. To our knowledge, this does not seem to be the case in this work.

6. *The Flight into Egypt* (altered from Seghers), (6th State), circa 1653

Etching with engraving and dry point
212 x 285 mm.; 8 3/8 x 11 1/4 inches

Watermark:
Countermark *IHS* (Ash & Fletcher No. 25-b, they refer to a *Flight into Egypt* 6th state in the Rijksmuseum's collection (OR116) with the same watermark and give a date of 1653)

Provenance:
P. Gellatly (Lugt 1185)
H. G. Gutekunst, Stuttgart, May 13-18, 1911: lot No. 870

References:
Bartsch/Hollstein 56
Hind 266-VI/VII
Barnard-Biörklund 53-2
New Hollstein 271-VI

Notes:
1. Unique in the artist's graphic oeuvre, in this work Rembrandt used the printing-plate of an engraving by Hercules Seghers (1590 - circa 1638) *Tobias and the Angel*, an etching after a painting by Adam Elsheimer (1578 - 1610). In six different states, (this appears to be an impression of the sixth state) Rembrandt completely reworked the right side of the plate, replacing it with a scene of *The Flight into Egypt*. Considered a monument in the history of landscape printmaking this is one of Rembrandt's most complex graphic works.

2. In the image, the remains of the angel's wings created by Seghers can be distinguished in the trees at the upper left, in sloping lines which fall diagonally from left to right. Preserved in all seven of Rembrandt's states, Seghers' little lizard, seen lower center, reminds us of Rembrandt's admiration of Seghers, an admiration further evidenced by Rembrandt's private collection which included eight Seghers paintings.

3. As printmakers and interpreters of landscape, the difference between the two artists' techniques is most clearly seen in their treatment of trees: Seghers' lightly treated, but very detailed trees on the left contrast with Rembrandt's more aggressive and fluid treatment of trees in the upper, right of this image.

4. The biblical reference here is*: Matthew* 2: 13-15

   When [the Magi] had departed, behold, the angel of the Lord appeared to Joseph in a Dream and said: "Rise, take the child and his mother, flee to Egypt, and stay there until I tell you. Herod is going to search for the child to destroy him". Joseph rose and took the child and his mother by night and departed for Egypt. He stayed there until the death of Herod, that what the Lord had said through the prophet might be fulfilled: "Out of Egypt I called my son".

5. The former owner of this work, Peter Gellatly (1831 - 1912), was a major 19th-century, London collector of Old Master prints (Dürer, Rembrandt).

7. *The Great Jewish Bride* (4th State), 1635

Etching, with some dry point and burin
219 x 168 mm.; 8 1/4 x 6 5/8 inches

Watermark:
Strasbourg Lily Coat of Arms with WR Countermark (Ash & Fletcher 36 A: Initials *Wra*)

Provenance:
Jan Six (1618-1700), according to the Rodolf Weigel Auction Catalogue, Leipzig, April 28, 1856: lot No. 467.
Herman Weber (Lugt 1383), Rodolf Weigel Auction Catalogue, Leipzig, April 28, 1856: lot No. 467.
Paul Davidsohn (Lugt 654) sold in Estate Auction, C. G. Boerner, Leipzig 26-27 April 1921.
Private German Collection since 1921.
Bassenge, Berlin, Auction 86, December 1-2, 2005: catalogue No. 5287.

References:
Bartsch 340
Hind 127-V/V
Barnard-Biörklund 35-C
New Hollstein 154-IV/V

Notes:
1. A very fine impression of one of Rembrandt's most complex works, combining etching, engraving (burin) and some drypoint.
2. New Hollstein notes diagonal lines added to the Bride's hands in the following fifth state.
3. The subject of this work has been widely debated, with various possible identifications indicated by scholars such as White-Boon. Valentiner proposed that the sitter was a stage actor, possibly Minerva, whereas Weisbach and Benesch suggest a Sibyl. M. Kahr (*Oud Holland*, 1966 (lxxxi), page 244 ff.) suggests the subject is Esther holding the decree, meditating over the slaying of the Jews.
4. White-Boon refer to Landsberger's study (*Rembrandt, the Jews and the Bible*, Philadelphia, 1946, page 74), where it was pointed out that a Jewish bride received her husband with her hair down and the *Ketubah* in her hand. The traditional title, however, is derived from the supposition that the sitter was the daughter of Ephraim Bonus, the subject of another of Rembrandt's famous etchings: *Ephraim Bonus, Jewish Physician*, 1647 (reference Bartsch, 278, our catalogue No. 18).
5. Past owners of this work included two major collectors: Herman Weber (1817 - 1854) and Berlin collector of Old Master prints Paul Davidsohn (born 1839).

8. *Jan Uytenbogaert, Preacher of the Remonstrants* (4th State), 1635

Etching with drypoint and engraving
225 x 187 mm.; 8 3/4 x 7 1/4 inches

Watermark:
Double-Headed Eagle (Ash & Fletcher No. 15-C.a.)

References:
Bartsch 279
Hind 128 IV/VI
Barnard-Biörklund 35-D
New Hollstein 153-IV/VI

Notes:
1. A very fine, rich, well-printed early impression of the fourth state (of six) of this work, one of Rembrandt's major portraits and the first officially commissioned of the artist. With considerable burr. On paper with a *Double-Headed Eagle* watermark. The same watermark is found on the fourth state impression of this work at the Art Institute of Chicago (Clarence Buckingham Collection, acquired in 1938, No. 1814) as well as on impressions of this work at the British Museum and on the fourth state at the Rijksmuseum.
2. In New Hollstein's fifth state, the irregular corners of the fourth state are made regular.
3. Rembrandt etched this portrait in 1635, when Uytenbogaert was seventy-eight years old. To be noted, Rembrandt had painted Uytenbogaert's portrait two years earlier (Rijksmuseum). This etched portrait is quite special in that by establishing a contrast between the brightly lit face and the dark background Rembrandt has created a confrontation between Uytenbogaert and us. He looks us directly in the eye.
4. An interesting description of Uytenbogaert is presented by Hinterding, (*Rembrandt The Printmaker,* Erik Hinterding, British Museum Press, 2000, page 144):

> The man portrayed is the preacher Johannes Uytenbogaert or Wtenbogaert (1557 - 1644), a distinguished and highly influential figure in his day. Shown at the age of seventy-eight, he was formerly Frederik Hendrik of Orange's tutor, and minister at the court of Prince Maurits. He became a leading spokesperson for and later the leader of the Remonstrants, a liberal movement in the Calvinist Church in opposition to the Counter-Remonstrants. An outspoken champion of religious tolerance, Uytenbogaert played a prominent role in the controversy between the two factions over the question of divine predestination. This theological dispute flared into a nationwide political struggle, reaching such proportions that Uytenbogaert was forced to flee Holland in 1618, after which he was officially banished. He returned in secret in 1626, once the situation had calmed down, and moved back into his old home in The Hague in 1629.

9. *Christ Driving the Money Changers from the Temple* (2nd State), 1635

Etching
136 x 169 mm.; 5 1/2 x 6 5/8 inches

Provenance:
Apparently Franz Pokorny, Vienna (Lugt 2763)
FR in a Cross (Unknown)

References:
Bartsch 69
Hind 126
Barnard-Biörklund 35-B
New Hollstein 139-II/IV

Notes:
1. A strong, well-printed, early impression.
2. In the New Hollstein's third state, Rembrandt added shadows to the lower left corner of the plate and lines to the left of the cow's right eye.
3. In this etching, Rembrandt closely followed the biblical reference from *Mark* 12, 15:

    ...They came to Jerusalem, and, on entering the temple area, he [Jesus] began to drive out those selling and buying there. He overturned the tables of the money changers and the seats of those who were selling doves. He did not allow anyone to carry anything through the temple area. Then he informed them saying:

    My house shall be called a house of prayer for all peoples. But you have made it a den of thieves...

Collection:
Private Collection, Illinois

10. *Adam and Eve* (2nd State), 1638

Etching
162 x 116 mm.; 6 3/8 x 4 9/16 inches

References:
Bartsch 28-II/II
Hind 159-II/II
Barnard-Biörklund 38-D
New Hollstein 168-II/II

Notes:
1. A very fine and early impression of the second state with the strengthened line in the foliage behind Adam. In the first state, that line is still light and not continuous.
2. Apparently for the first time in his graphic works, Rembrandt creates a landscape background, in this case, with an elephant roaming around. The serpent on the tree at right is clearly based on Dürer's *Christ in Limbo* of 1510, from Dürer's *Grosse Passion* (see image below). It appears that Rembrandt purchased an impression of that work, as well as an impression of Dürer's *Adam and Eve* on February 9, 1638 at the estate sale of Gommer Spranger (see: note 6 on page 139 of *Rembrandt the Printmaker,* London, Amsterdam, 2000). The two aforementioned works certainly influenced this print.
3. Contrary to its predecessors, Rembrandt's *Adam and Eve* depicts a more mature couple, versus the idealized youth in Dürer's *Adam and Eve.*

Dürer, *Adam and Eve* (2nd State), engraving, 1504

Dürer, *Christ in Limbo* (trial proof), woodcut, 1510

11. *The Large Lion Hunt* (1ˢᵗ State), 1641

Etching with drypoint
224 x 300 mm.; 8 7/8 x 11 3/4 inches

Provenance:
Cabinet Brentano-Birckenstock (Lugt 345)
F. Kalle (Lugt 1021)
Dr. Otto Schäfer (with stamp verso)

References:
Bartsch 114
Hind 181-II/IV
Barnard-Biörklund 41-D
New Hollstein 187-I/II

Notes:

1. A superb, early impression. Clear touches of burr are visible on the figures at extreme left and right as well as on the center fallen figure. With narrow margins and a few spots of foxing. Otherwise perfect.

2. In the New Hollstein's second state, the horse that is partly visible behind the horse on the extreme right is shaded with parallel lines.

3. Rembrandt's *The Large Lion Hunt* was possibly inspired by Pietro Testa (1611 - 1650) who has been described by A. Hyatt Mayor (*Prints & People*, 1971, No. 519) as the "most violent Italian painter-etcher" of his time. This "violence" is reflected in this etching, as various figures race in and out of the scene. On the other hand, Filedt Kok (*Rembrandt Etchings and Drawings in the Rembrandt House*, Maarsen, 1992, page 96) suggests that Rembrandt's inspiration for this etching came from the series of hunting scenes by Antonio Tempesta (1555 - 1630). Kok notes that Rembrandt's knowledge of Tempesta's work is well documented since "the 1656 inventory of Rembrandt's goods has four albums full of prints by Antonio Tempesta." Ger Luijten (*Rembrandt The Printmaker*, page 190) suggests that Tempesta's 1624 etching, *Lion Hunt*, executed only seventeen years before this work, inspired Rembrandt.

4. Johann Melchior Birckenstock (1738 - 1809) the former owner of this work was the Viennese founder of the Brentano-Birckenstock Collection. Birckenstock was the friend of the Old Master cataloguer Adam Bartsch as well as of the collector-expert Count von Fries as well as Duke Albert von Saxe-Teschen, the founder of the Albertina Collection in Vienna. After Birckenstock's death in 1809, the collection passed to his daughter Antonia (born in 1780) who then married Franz Brentano (1765 - 1844) also from Vienna and a professor at the University of Vienna. The collection later earned the designation Brentano-Birckenstock. Dr. Otto Schäfer, a more recent owner of this work, in our opinion, was Germany's most serious 20th-century collector of Old Master prints.

12. *Death of the Virgin* (2ⁿᵈ State), 1639

Etching with drypoint
409 x 315 mm.; 16 x 12 1/2 inches

Watermark:
Bekrönte Strassburger Lilie (Ash & Fletcher No. 36)

Provenance:
Pierre Mariette, Paris (Lugt 1788), 1667
R. S. Johnson Fine Art, 2013

References:
Bartsch 99-II/II
Hind 161 II/III
Barnard-Biorklund 39-A
New Hollstein 173-II/IV

Notes:
1. A very fine, richly inked, early impression of the second state (of three states), with the visible, full plate-line in this important and grandiose baroque composition. Collector's mark found on the verso of the signature of *Pierre Mariette, Paris* with the date of 1667, indicating that Mariette already owned this work two years before the death of Rembrandt. The *Bekönte Strassburger Lilie* watermark corresponds to Rembrandt impressions of the 1650s. In excellent condition. An outstanding example of this work.
2. In the following third state, New Hollstein notes additional shading above and below the canopy.
3. From a technical standpoint, this work is rich in contrasts. This is an early moment in the career of Rembrandt and the artist made extensive use of drypoint. This has resulted in the Baroque atmosphere created by the deep blacks in the lower left-side and the right-side of the composition, beautifully

Schongauer, *Death of the Virgin*, engraving, circa 1480

Dürer, *Death of the Virgin*, woodcut, 1510

  (text continues on page 34)

juxtaposed with the lightness in the clouds, angel and putti above. This sentiment for the baroque has been enhanced with the enormous curtain, which is used by Rembrandt as a "symbol of majesty".

4. Rembrandt has had a number of predecessors in the treatment of this scene. These include Van der Goes, Schongauer, Dürer and Bruegel. In Rembrandt's treatment of space in this work, one also thinks of Rubens who was born 29 years before Rembrandt and who was a master of the Baroque interior scene. Influences from Dürer include scenes from *The Life of the Virgin;* a series of woodcuts published in 1511, in particular *The Birth of the Virgin* and the *Death of the Virgin.* The "angel" above was probably inspired by Schongauer's *Death of the Virgin,* an engraving from about 1480, while the "acolyte" and his high-reaching cross, are direct descendents Dürer's *Death of the Virgin.* Rembrandt, had in fact just acquired an entire *Life of the Virgin* woodcut set from the sale of the collection of Gommer Spranger in Amsterdam in February of 1638, the year before the date of this work.

Collection:
Private Collection, Connecticut

13. *Christ Crucified Between Two Thieves* (oval plate, 2nd state), circa 1641

Etching
Plate: 136 x 102 mm.; 5 3/8 x 4 inches
Sheet: 144 x 108 mm.; 5 5/8 x 4 1/4 inches

Watermark:
Fragment of what appears to be a *Basilisk* watermark (Ash & Fletcher No. 12 Da)

Provenance:
John Barnard (Lugt 1419)
William Esdaile (Lugt 2617)
Sir John Dent (Lugt 2373)

References:
Bartsch 79-II/II
Hind 173
Barnard-Biörklund 41-2
New Hollstein 196-II/III

Notes:
1. An unusually fine and early impression of this moving work, with an outstanding provenance of John Barnard (b. 1784), William Esdaile (1758 - 1837) and Sir John Dent (b. 1884).
2. In the New Hollstein's second state, the square end of the cross in the forefront is rounded and narrowly misses the left border.
3. The biblical reference can be found in *Luke* 23, 29-43.

14. *The Small Lion Hunt (with two lions)* (2nd State), circa 1641

Etching with scraping
158 x 125 mm.; 6 1/16 x 4 13/16 inches

References:
Bartsch 115
Hind 180 II/II
Barnard-Biörklund 41-3
New Hollstein II/II

Notes:
1. A fine, well contrasted impression. On laid paper with thread margins around the full image. Hind distinguishes the first state as having the plate edges "irregular and dirty" while the second state has the "plate edges trimmed". From this description, this would be a second state. This impression, showing virtually no wear, has very strong scraping marks on the raised spear, with a quality of printing, which could only correspond to an early, lifetime example of this work. Except for one spot of discoloration on verso, in excellent condition.
2. Hind points out that it is possible that Rembrandt's heavy treatment of the foreground was used to cover up some earlier and still visible work on this plate.
3. As in Rembrandt's *Large Lion Hunt* (our catalogue No. 11), this work seems to be based on one of Antonio Tempesta's *Lion Hunts* (B. 11 33-39).
4. Elena Santiago Páez in her description of this work (*Rembrandt: La Lumière de l'ombre*, page 202) writes:

> This composition is typically baroque and it is composed as a theatrical scene, as was used by European painting during this period. This consists of creating a rather obscure foreground, a sort of barrier between the spectator and the primary scene, which takes place behind the foreground. In this case, the principle figure seems to be the horse approaching from the background, from the left and whose obscure coloration catches all our attention. A lion to the right prepares to attack the horse who looks at him, terrified. The resulting scene created possesses an overwhelming dynamism.

15. *The Triumph of Mordecai* (2nd State)*, circa 1641*

Etching with drypoint
173 x 214 mm., 6 7/8 x 8 1/2 inches

Watermark:
Pendant Initials WR, part of a *Strasbourg Bend* (Ash & Fletcher Cb, page 177 - appears to be the same watermark on the impression owned by the Museum of Fine Arts, Boston - MFA 56.293)

Provenance:
The Montclair Art Museum, Montclair, New Jersey

References:
Bartsch 40
Hind 172
Barnard-Biörklund 41-1
New Hollstein 185-II/IV

Notes:
1. A fine impression, with considerable burr on the figures and the architecture. The subject of this etching is inspired by *The Triumph of Mordecai,* an engraving by Lucas van Leyden (1515) and possibly the same subject, executed as a painting by Rembrandt's teacher, Pieter Lastman (1583 - 1633). In this second state, the tail of the horse is still not shaded. Apparently, this is one of the first etchings in which Rembrandt used drypoint extensively.
2. In the story, a disgraced Haman leads Mordecai through the streets. Ahasueras and Esther are watching the scene from the balcony of the city gate. To be noted, the city gate is the same as the gate found in Rembrandt's *The Nightwatch,* (his famous painting of 1642) and the King and Esther resemble Rembrandt and Saskia.
3. Rembrandt took this subject from the Old Testament (*Esther* 6):

> And it was found written, that Mordecai had told of Bigthana and Teresh, two of the king's chamberlains, of those that kept the door, who had sought to lay hands on the king Ahasuerus. And the king said: 'What honor and dignity hath been done to Mordecai for this?' Then said the king's servants that ministered unto him 'There is nothing done for him'. And the king said: 'Who is in the court?' Now Haman came into the outer court of the king's house, to speak unto the king to hand Mordecai on the gallows that he had prepared for him. And the king's servants said unto him: 'Behold, Haman standeth in the court.' And the king said 'Let him the come in.' So Haman came in. And the king said unto him 'What shall be done unto the man whom the king delighteth to honor?' Now Haman said in his heart 'Who would the king delight to honor besides myself?' And Haman said unto the king 'For the man whom the king delighteth to honor, let royal apparel be brought which the king useth to wear, and the horse that the king rideth upon, and on whose head a crown royal is set; and let the apparel and the horse be delivered to the hand of one of the king's most noble princes, that they may array the man therewith whom the king delighteth to honour, and cause him to ride on horseback through the street of the city, and proclaim before him: Thus shall it be done to the man whom the king delighteth to honour.' Then the king said to Haman 'Make haste, and take the apparel and the horse, as thou has said, and do even so to Mordecai the Jew, that sitteth at the king's gate; let nothing fail of all that thou hast spoken.' Then took Haman the apparel and the horse, and arrayed Mordecai, and caused him to ride through the street of the city, and proclaimed before him: 'Thus shall it be done unto the man whom the king delighteth to honour.'

16. *Landscape with the Three Trees*, 1643

Etching and drypoint
212 x 279 mm.; 8 3/4 x 11 1/8 inches

Watermark:
Strasbourg Lily E'.a. together with countermark *WK'a.* (Ash & Fletcher Nos. 36 and 26)

References:
Bartsch 212
Hind 205
Barnard-Biörklund 43-B
New Hollstein 214 I/I

Notes:
1. A very fine impression, with considerable burr.
2. Various art historians have described this work as Rembrandt's "greatest landscape print" to being "the greatest landscape in the history of printmaking". Ger Luijten, in his article on the 2001 Rembrandt exhibit at the Rijksmuseum (*Art on Paper*, May-June, 2001, page 46) describes *The Three Trees* as "by far the most elaborate and dramatic of the artist's landscape etchings." In this work, Rembrandt achieved a compositional tour de force, combining a dramatic landscape with unmatched atmospheric quality. The three trees are set horizontally against a view of Amsterdam (the dike on the right being the Diemerdijk or St. Anthonisdijk), with darkening clouds and an oncoming rainstorm. At the same time, the artist has juxtaposed vertically the brightest of skies above with the darkest of shadows and trees below. Hidden in the bushes is a pair of lovers. As much in the dark as their surrounding landscape, they appear oblivious to the extraordinary unfolding events going on directly over their heads.
3. In his *Landscape with Three Trees*, Rembrandt, in his use of etching and drypoint, has also achieved a formidable technical tour de force through the combination and reinforcement of one medium by another. The artist, in etching, laid out the entire basic design of this work. The most dramatic effects, however, are notably realized with drypoint, the storm effect above and to the left. The technical achievement of this work lies in the artist's masterful and sensitive juxtaposition of these two media. This same combination, however, presented the artist with complex technical problems in the actual printing from this plate. Even the slightest beginnings of wear, in the areas of drypoint in both the clouds above and the bushes and undergrowth below, forced the artist to ink this plate ever more strongly. The darker impressions plunged the two lovers in the bushes in the lower part of the composition into obscurity. It is certainly for the above reasons that Rembrandt printed only a small number of impressions from this plate since only such a small number would have been satisfactory for the artist.

17. *The Hog* (1ˢᵗ State), 1643

Etching and drypoint
147 x 186 mm.; 5 7/8 x 7 3/8 inches

Watermark:
Partially discernible watermark

Provenance:
Paul Davidsohn (Lugt 654)

References:
Bartsch 157
Hind 204-I/II
Barnard-Biörklund 43-A
New Hollstein 215

Notes:
1. A fine, early impression with burr of the first state of this extremely rare work. In the second state, Rembrandt added cross-hatching to the boy's face and the baby's earflap. For reference, one could compare the second state impression at the British Museum (illustrated on page 206 of *Rembrandt the Printmaker*) and the first state at the Fogg (No. 76 and reproduced on page 146 of *Rembrandt's Journey,* Museum of Fine Arts, Boston, 2003). In the second state, Hollstein indicates that the plate was cut, which is not the case with this present impression.
2. During this period, Rembrandt appeared to be fascinated with the keeping and slaughtering of hogs and produced a number of drawings on the subject. One of these drawings (Museé du Louvre, reference: Benesch 777) appears to be a direct study for this work.
3. The former owner of this work, Paul Davidsohn, was born in Danzig in 1839. Davidsohn was an avid collector of Old Master prints, and amassed over 10,000 works. His research on Old Master prints was considerable and was particularly important concerning the etchings of Adriaen van Ostade.

18. *The Omval*, (1st State) 1645

Etching and drypoint
184 x 225 mm.; 7 5/16 x 8 15 /16 inches

Watermark:
Initials, Countermark *WK*, (Ash & Fletcher No. 25)

Provenance:
Neville D. Goldsmid (Lugt 1962)

References:
Bartsch 209-I/II
Hind 210
Barnard-Biörklund 45-B
New Hollstein 221 I/II

Notes:

1. A very fine impression with considerable burr, typical of a first state. The second state, among other changes, is after the shortening of the brim of the hat of the man on the right. New Hollstein's reproductions appear to confirm that this is a first state.

2. In this impression, the hat of the man on the right is wider on the right than on the left. There is strong burr on the figure and boat on the right. All the above, according to White-Boon, is indicative of a first state.

3. This etching depicts a spot of land just outside of Amsterdam, still known as "The Omval". In the scene's center, there are several boats, which obscure The Omval Inn, seen in the distance. The larger two windmills stood on the Omval itself. To the left of the gnarled tree trunk, two lovers can be seen in the bushes, which recall the equally obscure hidden "lovers" found in the lower center of Rembrandt's *The Three Trees* of 1643 (our catalogue No. 16).

19. *Ephraim Bonus, Jewish Physician* (2nd State), 1647

Etching with drypoint and engraving
242 x 178 mm.; 9 1/2 x 7 inches

Watermark:
Basilisk (Ash & Fletcher No. 12 Aa)

Provenance:
John Malcolm of Poltalloch (1805 - 1893) (Lugt 1780)
British Museum Duplicate (Lugt 305)

References:
Bartsch 278
Hind 226
Barnard-Biörklund 47-A
New Hollstein 237 II/II

Notes:
1. A very fine impression of the second and final state. Strong burr from the drypoint appears on the balustrade, as well as on Ephraim's cloak. In this impression, the ring on Bonus' finger has been removed, indicative of a second state.
2. Ephraim Bonus was a Portuguese and Jewish physician translator and publisher of Hebrew writings. There is a preliminary study for this work in the in the Rijksmuseum (Bredins 252).
3. In his description in the Rembrandt House catalogue, Filedt Kok notes that in this work:

> The groundwork is laid in etching and the enormously varied superstructure is applied with burin (engraving) and drypoint. The drypoint work, which is fully integrated in Rembrandt's etching technique here for the first time was achieved in the shining velvet cloak.

Collection:
Private Collection, Oregon

20. *Self-Portrait Drawing at a Window* (3rd State), 1648

Etching, drypoint & burin
160 x 130 mm.; 6 1/4 x 5 1/8 inches

References:
Bartsch 22-III/V
Hind 229
Barnard-Biörklund 48-A
New Hollstein 240-III/IX

Notes:

1. Rembrandt depicted himself in many ways in his etched portraits. In *Self-Portrait with Plumed Cap and Lowered Sabre* of 1634 (Hind 100) and in his *Self-Portrait Leaning on a Stone Wall* of 1639 (Hind 168), he depicted himself not as an artist, but as an aristocrat, with all the trappings of an upper-class dandy. On the other hand, in this moving etching from 1648, *Self-Portrait Drawing at the Window*, we are presented with the artist hard at work, wearing a simple shirt, a painter's smock and a narrow-brimmed hat. Produced in his 40s, Rembrandt no longer looks very sure of himself, appearing worried, perhaps by his own art and concerned about the state of his life in general.

2. Sometime later (perhaps already in 1650), in the fourth state, a landscape was added by Rembrandt in the window. In earlier catalogues, this landscape was considered to have been contributed by another artist. This idea has been rejected as of late; the landscape is now attributed to the artist himself. In the Metropolitan Museum of Art's 1995 catalogue (page 211), Stephanie S. Dickey states that:

   "...the variety and inventiveness [in the fourth state] of the drypoint (seen for example, in the striated pattern added to the coat) are consistent with Rembrandt's work in the previous states and his approach in general...the handling of the vista recalls some of Rembrandt's landscape prints from about 1650, indicating that for this state, the master may have taken up this self-portrait again after an interval of a few years."

3. In the British Museum -Rijksmuseum's catalogue of 2000, Erik Hinterding reaffirms that the fourth state of this etching (with landscape added) was executed by Rembrandt, noting that (page 247): "impressions of the fourth state are often found with a *Strasbourg Lily* watermark, which is not found on prints of a later date

4. This extremely rare impression is before shading was added to the right hand and before a landscape was added in window, but with shading added on the left hand; clearly the New Hollstein's third state.

21. *The Hundred Guilder Print* (2nd State), circa 1649

Etching, drypoint & burin on *Japan* paper
278 x 388 mm.; 10 15/16 x 15 3/4 inches

Provenance:
Anonymous, initials *FP* in crayon verso, this impression cited by Lugt (reference Lugt 1039b).
P. Mathey (1844 - 1929), Paris (cf. Lugt 2100b)
A French monastery; Gutekunst & Klipstein, Bern, April 20, 1956, lot 167.
Dr. Otto Schäfer (1912-2000), Schweinfurt, Germany; Sotheby's New York, May 13, 1993, lot 17.
Sotheby's New York, May 3, 1996, lot 144.

References:
Bartsch 74 II/II
Hind 236
Barnard-Biörklund 49-1
New Hollstein 239-II/III

Notes:
1. A particularly fine, early and atmospheric impression on *Japan* paper, of New Hollstein's second, final state, with rich burr, wide margins, a subtle plate tone and inky plate edges. The former owner of this work, Dr. Otto Schäfer, is generally classed as Germany's most astute 20th-century collector of Old Master prints.
2. Since its creation, *Christ Healing the Sick* has been admired by many as Rembrandt's most ambitious, intricate and highly worked composition as a printmaker. Not only did he bring together a remarkably large number of figures in a complex and convincing composition, but also the print is a virtuoso display of his technical skills. By employing a combination of etching, drypoint and burin he succeeded in evoking a broad spectrum of tints, ranging from velvety black and light grey to almost white.
3. Stylistic differences between the groups of figures on the left and right, and frequent changes to the plate while in progress have given rise to the idea that Rembrandt worked on it intermittently over a decade. Recent research by Hinterding, however, has undermined this theory, and it is understood now that both groups of figures were started and completed in a relatively short time, near the end of the 1640s.
4. The plate exists in two states, the difference being minor changes to shadow passages in the background and hatching on the neck of the ass at the right. Rembrandt seems to have printed it almost exclusively on oriental paper – all of the nine-recorded impressions of the first state are on Japan paper, as are the majority of those in the second. This impression is one of twenty-eight known impressions on this paper, and is possibly the only one to remain in private hands.
5. Rather than depicting a single episode of Christ's preaching, Rembrandt chose to illustrate virtually all of *Matthew* XIX. From left to right are: the Pharisees with whom Christ debated the questions of marriage; the rich man He advised to sell his possessions to benefit the poor (the camel at right alluding to His observation that it was easier for a camel to pass through the eye of a needle than the rich to enter the Kingdom of Heaven); the children He asked to be brought to Him; the paralytic woman He healed. In the center, the etched figure of Christ visually holds the whole composition together.
6. There are several conflicting anecdotes as to how the informal title came about. The two most frequently cited are that Rembrandt swapped an impression for a group of prints by Marcantonio Raimondi (1480 - 1534) of this value (Rembrandt was a voracious print collector), another is that he paid this sum to buy back his own particularly fine, early impressions. However, a more believable explanation comes from a letter written by a 17th-century, Amsterdam print dealer, recommending it to a prospective purchaser as something of great value, which 'has been known to sell in Amsterdam for 100 Guilders or more'

22. *Jews in the Synagogue* (2nd State), 1648

Etching
73 x 132 mm.; 2 7/8 x 5 1/8 inches

References:
Bartsch 126
Hind 234
Barnard-Biörklund 48-D
New Hollstein 242-II/V

Notes:
1. A fine, well contrasted impression of the second state (of three states) before the vertical shading in the dark background had been added, a background clearly visible in the third state. This is one of Rembrandt's most expressive etchings, the genius of which is derived through the joining of the massive sculptural figures with powerful lighting effects of large and dark interiors.
2. Simon M. Schama in his essay: "A Different Jerusalem: The Jews in Rembrandt's Amsterdam" in *The Jews in the Age of Rembrandt* (Judaic Museum, Washington, D.C. 1981-1982) uses Rembrandt's etching *The Jews in the Synagogue* as the cover and also frontispiece of the publication. In his essay for this publication, Schama notes (page 3):

   …When not attired in the imaginary garb of Old Testament prophets and patriarchs, the Jews who figure in Dutch art are dressed indistinguishably from their Christian neighbors. Rembrandt's etching of *The Jews in the Synagogue* might be thought an exception, but the study seems drawn more from his imagination than any known locale, since its architecture resembles none of the Amsterdam temples… Instead of polarizing identities, Amsterdam's culture in those times tended to absorb [Jews] within its polyglot humanism…

3. The coat and hat of the man on the left are shaded, corresponding to a second state.

Collection:
Private Collection, Indiana

23. *Landscape with Three Gabled Cottages Beside a Road* (3ʳᵈ State), 1650

Etching and drypoint
161 x 202 mm.; 6 3/8 x 7 7/8 inches

References:
Bartsch 217 III/III
Hind 246
Barnard-Biörklund 50-D
New Hollstein 248-III/III

Notes:
1. A very fine impression with rich burr.
2. This work appears to relate to a pen, brown ink and wash drawing - *Cottages on the Schinkelweg, Looking towards the Overtoom,* now at the Kupferstichkabinett in Berlin (Benesch 835). The Overtoom was a bridge on the Schinkelcanal, not far from Amsterdam.
3. Rembrandt began this work in etching and then continued largely in drypoint. The drypoint additions continued through to the third state. In impressions such as this present one, the work in drypoint, with its extensive, rich and dramatic burr, simply overwhelmed the original composition. The uniqueness of this work originates in Rembrandt's ability in drypoint to display and combine aesthetically the seemingly sunlit scene in the background with what appears to be a clouded over, almost menacing foreground. The beauty and subtlety of this work makes it one of Rembrandt's greatest achievements in landscape printmaking.

24. *David in Prayer* (1ˢᵗ State), 1652

Etching

141 x 94 mm.; 5 5/8 x 3 3/4 inches

References:

Bartsch 41 I/III

Hind 258 I/III

Barnard-Biörklund 52-C

New Hollstein 268-I/III

Notes:

1. A fine, early impression of Hind's and New Hollstein's first state of three, with the short vertical stripe near upper left edge.

2. Rembrandt's biblical reference is (*II Samuel* 12: 15-16, The New English Bible Version):

    ...And the Lord struck the child that Uriah's wife bore unto David, and it was very sick. David went and therefore besought God for the child; and David fasted, and as often, as he went in, he lay all night upon the earth.

3. With respect to this and similar works, Jakob Rosenberg (page 176 of: *Rembrandt: Life and Work*, Phaidon Edition, Oxford, 1980) points out that:

    ...Rembrandt's Christianity was broad and evangelical. Certain fundamental notions such as [humility] and [suffering] he suggests with unparalleled depth of vision and power of expression. In his representation there is fully expressed the biblical humility which throws a man wholly upon God's mercy. This is completely at variance with the classic emphasis upon human strength and self-reliance, never quite abandoned by the typical Baroque painter...

4. In a similar vein, Rosenberg (page 58, see reference above) states that:

    ...Rembrandt seems to have regarded the vitality directed to the outside world and its enjoyment as of little consequence beside the more passive qualities of introspection, sympathy and humility.

25. *Christ Crucified between Two Thieves: The Three Crosses* (3rd State), 1653

Etching and drypoint
385 x 450 mm.; 15 1/4 x 17 3/4 inches

Watermark:
Strasburg Bend and Lily (Ash & Fletcher No. 35, D.a with 30 mm. wire lines)

Provenance:
A German Family of Title (Graf Plessen, Nehmten, Schleswig-Holstein)

References:
Bartsch 78-III/V
Hind 270-III/V
Barnard-Biörklund 53-A
New Hollstein 274-III/V (with signature and date in plate)

Notes:
1. Sophie de Bussierre (in her text for *La Collection Dutuit* shown in 1986 at the Petit Palais in Paris, page 201) wrote, "The final genius of Rembrandt as a printmaker, is crystallized in *the Three Crosses*". Whereas Ger Luijten, in his article in *Art on Paper* of May-June, 2001, wrote: "*The Three Crosses* is one of the undisputed high points in the history of printmaking."
2. A very fine, richly yet sensitively inked impression of the extremely rare third state (of five states); before the major alterations of the plate in the following fourth state. This early impression printed with considerable burr. The inking of the middle section of the image has been wiped very carefully and stands in splendorous contrast to the warm and vibrant tones of the side and lower portions of the sheet. Narrow to thread margins and inky plate lines. According to Hinterding (Eric Hinterding, *Rembrandt the Printmaker*, British Museum, 2000: page 302), there are seventeen (the number is now twenty-two) known impressions of the third state: two on vellum, the others, including this one, on *Strasburg Bend and Lily* watermarked western paper.

(text continues on page 60)

The Three Crosses (4th State), 1654
(after changing the direction of the horse)

3. The moment depicted in the third state is Christ's death as described in *Luke* 23, 44-46:

> It was now about the sixth hour. There was darkness over the whole land until the ninth hour, while the sun's light failed and the curtain of the temple was torn in two. Then, crying with a loud voice, Christ said: "Father, into thy hands I commit my spirit!" Having said this, he breathed his last.

4. In this scene, the "good" thief to the right, who confessed his repentance, is bathed in a "heavenly light" while the head of the "bad" thief remains in darkness. Christ's friends to the right are also illuminated brightly while those who demanded his death are in semi-groups. This scene, through both its monumentality and spirituality as well as for the personal vision expressed, is one of the most moving in the history of all the graphic arts. Rembrandt, using pure drypoint and burin cut directly into the plate. He first developed this grandiose conception in three states. In the third state, Rembrandt signed and dated the plate in 1653. In the following fourth state, Rembrandt made major changes to the composition, the most evident being the changed direction of the horse; in the third state the horse faces away from the dead or dying Christ, while in the fourth state the horse faces toward him.

26. *St. Jerome Reading in an Italian Landscape,* (2nd State), 1653

Etching, burin and drypoint
259 x 210 mm.; 10 1/4 x 8 1/4 inches

Watermark:
Foolscap Fb. (Ash & Fletcher No. 19)

References:
Bartsch 104
Hind 267-II/II
Barnard-Biörklund 53-C
New Hollstein 275-II/II

Notes:
1. A fine impression of this major work, one of the most rare and most important in the graphic oeuvre of Rembrandt. With burr from the drypoint in the background to the right, in the tree trunks to the left, in the branches upper left and in the mane of the lion. The struts of the bridge on the right have been redrawn, making this a second state.
2. The *Foolscap fb.* watermark is quite close to Churchill 341 (dated 1644) and Churchill 345 (dated 17th century). Nancy Ash and Shelley Fletcher (*Watermarks in Rembrandt's Prints*) note an identical or nearly identical watermark in two impressions of *St. Jerome Reading in an Italian Landscape* in the Print Collection of the Rijksmuseum (reference OB: 120 and RH: duplicate) and still another at the Pierpont Morgan Library.
3. St. Jerome was one of the four Fathers of the Church. As in this work, he generally is depicted as a recluse accompanied by a lion. Rembrandt etched St. Jerome seven different times over a period of twenty-six years, between 1627 and 1653. The first of these was *St. Jerome Kneeling, Large Plate,* 1627 (Bartsch 106); the second, *St. Jerome Praying, Arched,* 1632 (Bartsch 101); the third, *St. Jerome Reading,* 1634)(Bartsch 100); the fourth, *St. Jerome Kneeling in Prayer, Looking Down,* 1635 (Bartsch 102); the fifth, *St. Jerome in a Dark Chamber,* 1642 (Bartsch 105); the sixth, *St. Jerome Beside a Pollard Willow,* 1648 (Bartsch 103); this is the last and, as we judge it, the most beautiful of these studies *St. Jerome Reading in an Italian Landscape,* 1653 (Bartsch 104). Rembrandt's great interest in St. Jerome is possibly explainable by the number of 16th century prints and drawings of this subject, which Rembrandt either saw or owned. Or perhaps Rembrandt's interest came from his respect for St. Jerome as the "father of humanism".

27. *Christ at Emmaus (The Large Plate),* (1st State), 1654

Etching, burin and drypoint
209 x 159 mm.; 8 1/4 x 6 1/4 inches

Watermark:
Seven Provinces (cf. Heawood 3142)

References:
Bartsch 87
Hind 282
Barnard-Biörklund 54-H
New Hollstein 283 I/III

Notes:
1. A fine impression of the first state (of three) with the rays encircling Christ's head only partly drawn.
2. On Easter Sunday, the third day after his death, Christ rose from the grave. He remained on earth for forty days, until his ascension into heaven. During this period, Christ met two of his disciples on the road from Jerusalem to Emmaus. He joined them and they spoke to him but did not recognize him. The following scene is described in *Luke,* 24: 28-31:

> By this time they were nearing Emmaus and the end of the journey. Jesus would have gone on, but they begged him to stay the night with them, as it was getting late. So he went home with them. As they sat down to eat, he asked God's blessing on the food and then took a small loaf of bread and broke it and was passing it over to them when suddenly - it was as though their eyes were opened - they recognized Him! And at that moment he disappeared.

3. This is one of Rembrandt's most fascinating compositions. There is the parallel between the position of Christ here and that of Leonardo da Vinci's Christ in the *Last Supper* (1495–1498). However, in the latter, there are thirteen figures while in this etching only four. In Rembrandt's etching, the three figures surrounding Christ form an interesting contrast. Recognizing Christ, the figure at left falls into an attitude of prayer and contemplation; the figure at right shows still total astonishment, while the figure in the foreground apparently has not yet grasped the meaning or significance of the scene in front of him.

Collection:
Private Collection, Pennsylvania

28. *The Descent from the Cross by Torchlight*, (1st State), 1654

Etching with drypoint
205 x 161 mm. (sheet: 218 x 169 mm.); 8 x 6 3/8 inches (sheet: 8 1/2 x 6 5/8 inches)

References:
Bartsch 83
Hind 280
Barnard-Biörklund 54-G
New Hollstein 286 I/IV

Notes:

1. A fine, early impression with burr on the figure pulling down the sheet and on the figure supporting Christ's body, on Christ's neck, and elsewhere. Before dots added in the upper-right hand corner, all indicative of a first state.

2. This scene relates to the description of *Matthew* (XXVII, 57-59):

> When it was evening, there came a rich man from Arimathea named Joseph who was himself a disciple of Jesus. He went to Pilate and asked for the body of Jesus; then Pilate ordered it to be handed over. Taking the body, Joseph wrapped it in clean linen and laid it in his new tomb that he had hewn in the rock. Then he rolled a huge stone across the entrance to the tomb and departed. But Mary Magdalene and the other Mary remained sitting there, facing the tomb...

3. In his interpretation of this subject, Rembrandt has infused it with an emotional intensity characteristic of his later works. The emotional qualities of this scene are transmitted not only by the pictorial elements involved, but also by the technique Rembrandt used. The broad and powerfully etched lines, as well as the dramatic shadows created with drypoint, deepen the impact of the image. The hopelessness of the situation is conveyed through the darkest shadows. Rembrandt's emotion is expressed not simply through the figures, but also through the expertly achieved use of light and shadow. The dramatic content of this scene is presented through the stark contrast between the dark night and the force of the white shroud awaiting the body of Christ as well as the large and powerfully etched drypoint lines used to present the scene.

29. *Abraham's Sacrifice*, 1655

Etching and drypoint

156 x 130 mm. (sheet: 164 x 135 mm.) 6 1/8 x 5 1/8 inches (sheet: 6 1/2 x 5 3/8 inches)

References:

Bartsch 35

Hind 283

Barnard-Biörklund 55-B

New Hollstein 287

Notes:

1. A fine early impression, with burr evident in the logs beneath the bowl, as well as to the right of the bowl.

2. Rembrandt followed the iconographical tradition in depicting the angel grasping Abraham's arm instead of following the biblical text in which the angel only calls out to Abraham. The scene is described in the *Old Testament, Genesis* 22:1-3, 9-13:

> Later on God tested Abraham's faith and obedience...God called...Take with you your only son - Isaac, whom you love so much- and go to the land of Moriah and sacrifice him there as a burnt offering upon one of the mountains which I'll point out to you... When they arrived at the place where God had told Abraham to go, he built an altar and placed the wood in order, ready for the fire, and then tied Isaac and laid him on the altar over the wood. And Abraham took the knife and lifted it up to plunge it into his son, to slay him.

> At that moment an Angel shouted to him from heaven: Abraham, Abraham...Lay down the knife, don't hurt the lad in any way, the Angel said, for I know that God is first in your life - you have not withheld even your beloved son from him. Abraham then noticed a ram caught by its horns in a bush. So he took the ram and sacrificed it, instead of his son, as a burnt offering on the altar.

3. The principle figure of Abraham is defined in the strict and simple forms of Rembrandt's style of the 1650s. Jan Filedt Kok (*Rembrandt's Etchings & Drawings in the Rembrandt House*, page 43) notes "the three figures of the central group are merged into a compact form nearly resembling a sculpture in the round." On the other hand, "the bright peaceful view into the distant background and the waiting servants with their donkey form a strong contrast with the main figures." A powerful shaft of Baroque-inspired light illuminates these latter figures, shrouded in darkness.

30. *Jan Lutma, Goldsmith* (2ⁿᵈ State), 1656

Etching and drypoint
196 x 148 mm.; 5 7/8 x 7 3/4 inches

References:
Bartsch 276
Hind 290-II/III
Barnard-Biörklund 56-C
New Hollstein 293-II/V

Notes:

1. Jan Lutma the Elder, a well-known gold and silversmith, was born in Groningen in 1584 and died in 1669. He was active in Amsterdam from 1621 on. In this etching, the objects on the table beside Lutma refer to his trade: a silversmith's hammer, a cup with punches and a chased silver basin with ornamental lobe. In the sitter's hand, there appears to be a statue or candlestick. Rather than emerging from darkness, like so many of Rembrandt's portraits, the figure and its background are suffused with light. Ackley (Clifford S. Ackley, *Printmaking in the Age of Rembrandt*, Museum of Fine Arts, Boston, 1980: pp. 203-204) notes that the sitter here "looks downward or inward, his brow wrinkled in thought". Ackley feels that Rembrandt's use of shadow:

    "...Makes Lutma's expression ambiguous and mobile, suggesting a range of possible interpretations and hinting at human complexity. This sense of interior meditation and intellectual life is one of Rembrandt's most remarkable contributions to portraiture".

2. A very fine second state impression, before the additions in the upper right-hand corner found in the third state.

Collection:
Private Collection, Oxford, England.

31. *Lieven Willemsz van Coppenol: Writing Master: Smaller Plate,* (3rd State) 1658

Etching and drypoint
258 x 190 mm.; 10 1/4 x 7 1/2 inches

References:
Bartsch 282-II/III
Hind 269
Barnard-Biörklund 58-1
New Hollstein 305-III/VI

Notes:
1. A fine impression of the rare third state of this etching/drypoint. The first state is before the addition of the compass and shading to Coppenol's right hand and quill pen. Other impressions of this state can be found in the Rijksmuseum, Amsterdam (2); Kupferstichkabinett, Berlin; The British Museum, London; Hermitage Museum, St. Petersburg and the Albertina in Vienna.
2. In the second state, the compass is added to the wall beside the window. Shading is added to Coppenol's hands, the quill pen and the candle. The circular disk in the right background is worked over and darkened. Impressions of this state can be found in the Rijksmuseum, Amsterdam (2); Kupferstichkabinett, Berlin; The British Museum, London; the Pierpont Morgan Library in New York; Hermitage Museum, St. Petersburg and the Dutuit Collection in Paris.
3. In the third state, fine, vertical and diagonal shading is added to Coppenol's forehead, and to his right cheek. Shading is also added to the boy's head and the lower part of his collar. Impressions of this state can be found in the Rijksmuseum, Amsterdam; Fitzwilliam Museum, Cambridge; The British Museum, London; Hermitage Museum, St. Petersburg; Ashmolean Museum, Oxford; Bibliothèque Nationale, Paris; Rothschild Collection, Paris and the Albertina in Vienna.
4. Coppenol was born in 1598 and died in 1671. Until 1650, he directed *l'École Française* of Amsterdam. He concentrated his interests in calligraphy. He had a certain reputation from having traveled all over Holland in an automobile which he called his "verger" in which he kept his own most beautiful examples of calligraphy. One of Coppenol's main objectives in life was to be portrayed by the most highly regarded artists of his time: these included Rembrandt, the engraver Cornelis Visscher, and the sculptor Arthur Quellinus. Coppenol also solicited the most famous poets to create poems in his honor.

No. 19 **Ephraim Bonus** (detail), 1647